TREASURE CHEST
For English Language Learners

Practice Book

Macmillan
McGraw-Hill

B

The *McGraw·Hill* Companies

 **Macmillan
McGraw-Hill**

Published by Macmillan/McGraw-Hill, of McGraw-Hill Education, a division of The McGraw-Hill Companies, Inc.,
Two Penn Plaza, New York, New York 10121.

Printed in the United States of America

2 3 4 5 6 7 8 9 021 09 08 07

Contents

Name _____

Write a word from the box to complete each sentence.

| up | jump | down | not |

_____

1. She can _____.

_____

2. Bird can fly _____.

_____

3. Frog can jump _____.

_____

4. He is _____ sad.

© Macmillan/McGraw-Hill

Name _____

Circle the characters in the story <u>Cat Can Jump</u>.

cat

puppy

bird

Write a word from the box to tell about the picture.

| jump | tree | down |

I. Where is the cat?

_____

The cat is in the _____.

2. Why is the cat sad?

_____

The cat can not _____.

3. Does the cat get down?

_____

Yes, the cat gets _____.

Name _____

Circle the word that names the picture.
Write the word on the line.

1.

rat   nut

_____

- - - - - - - - -

_____

2.

man   map

_____

- - - - - - - - -

_____

3.

pan   pad

_____

- - - - - - - - -

_____

4.

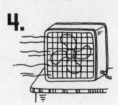

fan   ant

_____

- - - - - - - - -

_____

Name _____

Write a word from the box to complete each sentence.

over	too	it	yes

_____

\- - - - - - - - - - -

1. Can she throw the ball? _____ .

_____

\- - - - - - - - - - -

2. She can kick the ball, _____ .

_____

\- - - - - - - - - - -

3. She hits the ball. She hits _____ .

_____

\- - - - - - - - - - -

4. She hits the ball _____ .

Name _____

Circle the words that make a sentence.

1. Bird down and up.   Bird can fly.

2. Bat can not jump.   Bat not fly.

3. Rabbit can jump.   Rabbit you too.

4. Girl fly.   Girl can not fly.

Name _____

Circle the word that names the picture.
Write the word on the line.

1.

hat   bat

_____

- - - - - - - - - -

_____

2.

man   van

_____

- - - - - - - - - -

_____

3.

tennis   lamp

_____

- - - - - - - - - -

_____

4.

back   tack

_____

- - - - - - - - - -

_____

Name _____

Look at the pictures.
Write the numbers 1, 2, or 3 to show the order.

_____   _____   _____

_ _ _ _ _ _ _ _ _   _ _ _ _ _ _ _ _ _   _ _ _ _ _ _ _ _ _

_____   _____   _____

Write a word from the box to complete each sentence.

| runs   hits   throws |

_____
_ _ _ _ _ _ _ _ _

4. First, he _____ the ball.

_____
_ _ _ _ _ _ _ _ _

5. Then, she _____ the ball.

_____
_ _ _ _ _ _ _ _ _

6. Last, she _____ fast.

Name _____

Circle the sentence that has words in the correct order.

1. Baseball fun is.

   Baseball is fun.

2. Too you can play.

   You can play too.

Draw an X over the word that does not belong in each sentence.

3. He plays to basketball.

4. I is like soccer.

Draw a line to match the word to the picture.

1. skates

2. rides

3. runs

Write a word from above to complete each sentence.

4. She _____ fast.

5. The boy _____ a bike.

Name _____

The word <u>hit</u> has the short <u>i</u> sound.
Circle the words that sound like <u>hit</u>.

1.	quit	too	much
2.	run	is	kite
3.	bike	wig	bug
4.	six	ball	safe

Circle the word that names the picture.
Write the word on the line.

5.

pig   kid

_____

- - - - - - - - - - - -

6.

dish   sand

_____

- - - - - - - - - - - -

Name _____

Look at the pictures.
Write the numbers 1, 2, or 3 to show the order.

_____   _____   _____

- - - - - - - -   - - - - - - - -   - - - - - - - -

_____   _____   _____

Write a word from the box to complete
each sentence.

> walk   crawl

_____

- - - - - - - - -

4. The baby can _____.

_____

- - - - - - - -

5. The girl can _____.

Circle the sentence that is a statement.

1. She can ride.

   Can she skate?

2. Can you come to my house?

   I will come to your house.

Write a word from the box to complete each statement.

| rides   jump |

3. Can the horse jump?
   _____

   - - - - - - - - - -
   Yes, the horse can _____.

4. Does he ride the bus?
   _____

   - - - - - - - - - -
   Yes, he _____ the bus.

Name _____

Circle the sentence that tells about each picture.

1. The dog eats.

The good dog sleeps.

2. Come here, Cat!

The cat sleeps.

Read the sentences. Circle the picture that matches the sentence.

3. The pie is on the table.

4. That cat is on the chair.

Name _____

Circle the words with blends <u>gr</u> or <u>tr</u>.

1. great   boy   train

2. ride   treat   good

Circle the word that names the picture. Write the word on the line.

3. grass   apple

    _____

    _ _ _ _ _ _ _ _ _

    _____

4. drink   sleep

    _____

    _ _ _ _ _ _ _ _ _

5. treat   nap

    _____

    _ _ _ _ _ _ _ _ _

Amy gives the cat a _____.

Name _____

Circle the cat in each picture. Write a word from the box to complete each sentence.

| tree | grass | bedroom |

1. The cat plays in the _____.

2. The cat hides in the _____.

3. The cat is in the _____.

Circle the characters in the story <u>Good Cat!</u>

© Macmillan/McGraw-Hill

Name _____

Look at the end of each sentence.
Is the ? or ! correct? Circle <u>yes</u> or <u>no</u>.

1. Do you like pets?   yes   no

2. I love pets?   yes   no

3. Do you have a new cat!   yes   no

4. Yes, I have a new cat!   yes   no

Read the sentences. Write a ! or ? on the line.

5. This cat is heavy ___

6. Is the cat on the bed ___

Name _____

Write <u>now</u> or <u>use</u> to complete each sentence.

1. We can help _____ .

2. I _____ a brush to wash the dishes.

Draw a line to match the sentence to the picture.

3. He can clean.

4. She can clean.

Name _____

The word <u>sink</u> has the <u>nk</u> sound.
Circle the words that sound like <u>sink</u>.

1. rink   rug

2. tree   tank

3. grass   bunk

Use a word from the box to name each picture. Write the word on the line.

| ant   hand   nest |

4. _____

5. _____

6. _____

Think about the story, <u>We Help!</u>
Circle the sentences that tell about the story.

1. Children can sleep.

   Children can help.

2. Children can clean the car.

   Children can run.

3. Children can talk.

   Children can wash dishes.

4. Children can eat.

   Children can wash the dog.

Name _____

**Look for capital letters and end marks.
Circle the correct sentence.**

1. the dog runs

   The dog runs.

2. Is the sink clean

   Is the sink clean?

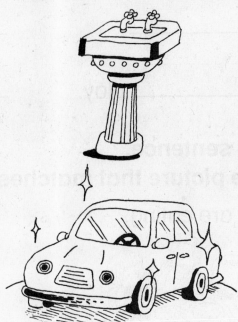

3. The car is clean.

   The car is clean

4. Children can clean the park.

   Children can clean the park

Name _____

Circle the word that completes each sentence. Write the word on the line.

1.

Two   They

_____

- - - - - - - - - - -

_____ play.

2.

One   Boy

_____

- - - - - - - - - - -

_____ girl plays.

Read the sentence. Circle the picture that matches the sentence.

3. They are eating.

4. Two boys are walking.

Name _____

Think about the story, <u>Little Lions</u>.
Circle the sentences that tell about the story.

1. **Main Idea:**

   Little lions can do many things.

   Little lions can walk.

2. **Detail 1:**

   Little lions have fur.

   Little lions sleep.

3. **Detail 2:**

   Little lions run.

   Little lions have tails.

4. **Detail 3:**

   Little lions have big paws.

   Little lions play.

Circle the word that sounds like <u>box</u>.
Write the word on the line.

1.

tree   mop

_____
- - - - - - - - - - - -
_____

2.

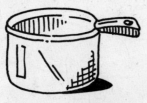

pot   pick

_____
- - - - - - - - - - - -
_____

3.

fox   bear

_____
- - - - - - - - - - - -
_____

4.

rock   fall

_____
- - - - - - - - - - - -
_____

© Macmillan/McGraw-Hill

Name _____

Draw a line to match the sentence to the picture.

1. Is the bear sleeping? No.

2. Some girls jump.

Circle the word that completes each sentence.
Write the word on the line.

_____

3. He _____ eggs.

   who   eats

_____

4. _____ is this boy?

   yes   Who

Name _____

Circle the noun that names the picture.

1.

lion   run

2.

play   grass

Circle a noun to complete the sentence.
Write the word on the line.

3. Lions drink _____ _____.

    sleep   water

4. I help my _____ _____.

    run   mom

Name _____

Circle the word that names the picture.
Write the word on the line.

1. _____
   - - - - - - - - - -
   _____

   egg   nose

2. _____
   - - - - - - - - - -
   _____

   bed   truck

The word <u>hen</u> has the short <u>e</u> sound.
Circle the word that sounds like <u>hen</u>.

3. I like to sled.

4. This is a dress.

Name _____

Circle the sentences that retell <u>Farm Animals</u>.

1. Pigs live on a farm.

   Bears live on a farm.

2. Hens live on a farm.

   Fish live on a farm.

3. The cow has eggs.

   The hen has eggs.

4. The boy eats the eggs.

   The dog eats the eggs.

Circle the plural noun that names each picture.

1. bird   birds

2. socks   sock

3. boy   boys

Circle the plural noun that completes each sentence. Write the word on the line.

4. I see two _____.
   hen   hens

5. I see some _____.
   eggs   egg

Name _____

Draw a line to match each sentence to the picture.

I. The fish lives in water.

2. Many birds fly out of the tree.

Write a word from the box to complete each sentence.

| lives   many |

_____

3. The bear _____ in the forest.

_____

4. There are _____ eggs.

© Macmillan/McGraw-Hill

Name _____

Circle the word that sounds like <u>she</u>.

1.   some   shell

2.   shirt   same

Circle the word that sounds like <u>thin</u>.

3.   three   two

4.   tap   throw

Name _____

Think about the story, <u>In the Forest</u>.
Circle the sentences that tell about the story.

1. Main Idea:

Many animals live in the forest.

Many animals live in water.

2. Detail 1:

Owls live in the forest.

Fish live in the forest.

3. Detail 2:

Cows live in the forest.

Bears live in the forest.

4. Detail 3:

Rabbits live in the forest.

Hens live in the forest.

Name _____

Draw a line to match the plural noun to the picture.

1. mice

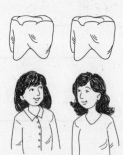

2. teeth

3. women

Circle the word that names the picture.

4.   foot   feet

5.   child   children

Name _____

Write a word from the box to complete each sentence.

> three   want

_____

1. We _____ to do a show.

_____

2. _____ children play.

Circle the sentence that matches each picture.

3. They play.   He puts on a mask.

4. Three friends read.   Two friends talk.

Circle the word that names the picture.

1. bug   bow

2. tube   truck

3. brush   boy

Circle the words that sound like <u>gum</u>.
Write the word on the line.

4. The cub is small. _____

5. He shuts the door. _____

Name _____

Circle the sentences that retell <u>A Show for Us</u>.

1. Beginning

Three friends see a show.

Three friends see a band.

2. Middle

Pam wants to eat.

Pam wants to do a show.

3. End

The friends act in a show.

The friends read a book.

© Macmillan/McGraw-Hill

Underline the proper nouns.
Circle the correct sentence.

1. Mrs. Chin teaches.

   mrs. chin teaches.

2. Sam and Andy are friends.

   Sam and andy are friends.

Write the proper noun to complete each sentence.

3. _____ plays the drums.

   dan   Dan

4. _____ can dance.

   Rita   rita

5. Her name is _____ .

Name _____

Circle the word that completes each sentence. Write the word on the line.

1. _____

   _____ is Monday.

   Today   bus

2. _____

   I go to _____ on Monday.

   dog   school

Write a word from the box to complete each sentence.

Why	late

3. _____

   Oh no! I am _____!

4. _____

   _____ is she happy?

© Macmillan/McGraw-Hill

Name _____

Draw a line to match the words to the pictures.

1. glass

2. clock

3. plate

Write a word from the box that names each picture.

plant   blocks

4.

5.

_____

- - - - - - - - - -

_____

- - - - - - - - - -

Name _____

Circle the sentence that tells the order of events in Clem Goes to School.

I. First:

First, Glen plays.

First, Glen takes Clem to school.

2. Next:

Next, Clem takes Glen to school.

Next, Clem paints.

3. Last:

In the end, Clem draws.

In the end, Clem plays.

Underline the proper nouns.
Circle the correct sentence.

1. It is warm in July.

   It is warm in july.

2. I go to school on monday.

   I go to school on Monday.

3. I play soccer on wednesdays.

   I play soccer on Wednesdays.

4. Thanksgiving is in November.

   thanksgiving is in november.

Name _____

Circle the word that completes each sentence. Write the word on the line.

1. _____ ! The kite is in the sky.

   Can   Oh

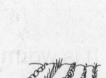

2. Look at _____ the plants.

   all   two

3. _____ you help me?

   Could   Wagon

4. Yes, I can _____ the wagon!

   play   pull

Name _____

Circle the word that names the picture.
Write the word on the line.

1. _____

   cake   shoe

2. _____

   water   wave

3. _____

   pig   plate

4. _____

   green   grape

Name _____

Look at each picture. Circle the word that tells what happens next. Write the word on the line.

_____

1. She will _____ the fish some food.

   give   food

_____

2. He will _____ the plates on the table.

   read   put

_____

3. He will _____ a letter.

   read   write

Draw a picture to show what will happen next.

© Macmillan/McGraw-Hill

Circle the word that is a verb in the sentence.

1. The children pull a wagon.

   pull   wagon

2. The dog runs away.

   runs   dog

3. The girl brings flowers.

   flowers   brings

Write the verb in each sentence on the line.

4. He gives the plant water. _____

5. She opens the window. _____

Name _____

Write a word from the box to complete each sentence.

| together girls |

_____

- - - - - - - - - - - -

1. The boys are playing _____.

_____

- - - - - - - - - -

2. The _____ are flying kites.

Draw a line to match the word to the picture.

3. boy   a.

4. water   b.

Name _____

Circle the word that names the picture.
Write the word on the line.

1.

2.

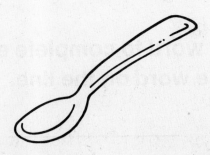

slide   sat   spoon   hat

_____   _____

- - - - - - - - - - - - -   - - - - - - - - - - - - -

_____   _____

Circle the words with the <u>s</u> blend sound.

3.   spoil   slow   table

4.   paper   drum   snail

5.   star   hat   smell

6.   boat   swap   slice

Name _____

Circle <u>yes</u> or <u>no</u> to answer the questions.

1. Do both girls have a drum?   yes   no
2. Do both girls have a flag?   yes   no
3. Are both girls wearing hats? yes   no

Circle a word to complete each sentence.
Write the word on the line.

_____

_ _ _ _ _ _ _ _ _ _ _

4. Annie is _____ than Ben.

      taller   shorter

_____

_ _ _ _ _ _ _ _ _ _ _

5. The elephant is _____ than the lion.

      bigger   smaller

Circle the verb in the sentence.

1. The child swims in the pool.

2. He plays in the water.

3. He runs to the pool.

Write a word from the box to complete each sentence.

listens	walks	talks	plays

_____

4. Ellen _____ the drum.

5. Her friend _____ to music.

6. Micah _____ in the park.

7. He _____ with his friend.

Name _____

Draw a line to match each sentence to a picture.

1. These are our shadows.

2. Your shadow is really big!

3. The light is bright today.

Label the picture with the words light and shadows.

Name _____

Circle the word that comp
Write the word on the line

1. Hi Lara, _____

    how   why

2. Hi Eric. Can you _____

    call   see

3. Do you need _____

    more   are

4. I have _____

    it   so

Name _____

Draw a line under the words that sound like <u>rich</u> and <u>itch</u>.

1.   sink   match   duck

2.   lunch   boot   puppy

3.   face   patch   shoe

Circle the word that completes each sentence.
Write the word on the line.

_____

4. _____ pet is your favorite?

   Which   Sleep

_____

5. We play_____ with a tennis ball.

   who   catch

_____

6. My dog likes to_____ balls, too!

   fetch   eat

© Macmillan/McGraw-Hill

Name _____

Read the story. Circle the answers to the qu‌verb in each sentence.

Light makes shadows.

All things have shadows.

The sun is out. We see shadows.

The sun is not out. We do not see shadows.

1. What is the story about?

   clouds   shadows

2. What makes shadows?

   light   dark

3. Do all things have shadows?

   yes   no

4. Do we see shadows when the sun is not ou

   yes   no

ys played on the beach.

ked to her friends.

ked to school.

b from the box to complete each sentence.

| bed | played | turned |

_____ me later?

_____ soccer after school.

_____ time?

_____ the page.

_____ the hill.

Name _____

Draw a line under the words that sound like rich and itch.

I. sink   match   duck

2. lunch   boot   puppy

3. face   patch   shoe

Circle the word that completes each sentence. Write the word on the line.

_____

4. _____ pet is your favorite?

   Which   Sleep

5. We play _____ with a tennis ball.

   who   catch

6. My dog likes to _____ balls, too!

   fetch   eat

Name _____

Read the story. Circle the answers to the questions.

Light makes shadows.

All things have shadows.

The sun is out. We see shadows.

The sun is not out. We do not see shadows.

1. What is the story about?

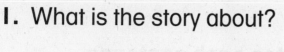

   clouds   shadows

2. What makes shadows?

   light   dark

3. Do all things have shadows?

   yes   no

4. Do we see shadows when the sun is not out?

   yes   no

Name _____

Circle the verb in each sentence.

1. The boys played on the beach.

2. She talked to her friends.

3. He walked to school.

Write a verb from the box to complete each sentence.

| climbed | played | turned |

_____

4. He _____ soccer after school.

_____

5. He _____ the page.

_____

6. Sara _____ the hill.

Name _____

Circle the word that completes each sentence. Write the word on the line.

_____

1. Hi Lara, _____ are you?

how   why

_____

_ _ _ _ _ _ _ _ _ _ _

2. Hi Eric. Can you _____ me later?

call   see

_____

_ _ _ _ _ _ _ _ _ _ _

3. Do you need _____ time?

more   are

_____

_ _ _ _ _ _ _ _ _ _ _

4. I have _____ many things to tell you!

it   so

Name _____

Circle the word that names the picture.
Write the word on the line.

1. _____

   _____

   jar   fire

2. _____

   _____

   kite   skate

The word <u>ice</u> has the long <u>i</u> sound.
Circle the words that sound like <u>ice</u>.

3.   time   catch   is

4.   it   pit   mice

5.   are   slide   late

6.   shine   cold   happy

Look at the picture. Circle <u>yes</u> or <u>no</u> to tell what will happen next.

1. Will he go to school?

   yes   no

2. Will he ride his bike to school?

   yes   no

3. Will Billy play baseball?

   yes   no

4. Will Billy have a surprise party?

   yes   no

5. Will they get a new puppy?

   yes   no

6. Will they go swimming?

   yes   no

Name _____

Circle the word to complete each sentence.
Write the word on the line.

1. These hats _____ nice.

   _____
   - - - - - - - - - -

   is   are

2. Yes, the hats _____ nice.

   _____
   - - - - - - - - - -

   is   are

3. This watch _____ also nice.

   _____
   - - - - - - - - - -

   is   are

4. Yes, that watch _____ nice.

   _____
   - - - - - - - - - -

   is   are

5. _____ we going to buy it?

   _____
   - - - - - - - - - -

   Is   Are

Name _____

Circle the word that completes each sentence. Write the word on the line.

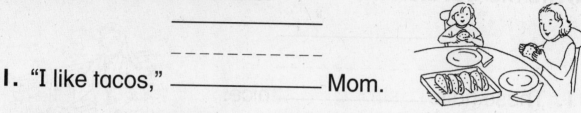

1. "I like tacos," _____ Mom.

    say   says

2. "I like them too!" I _____.

    says   say

3. I _____ my cat some food.

    give   help

4. We _____ a story after dinner.

    do   read

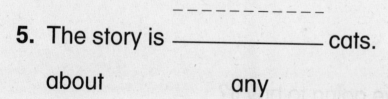

5. The story is _____ cats.

    about   any

Name _____

Write a word from the box to name each picture. Circle the letters that make the str sound in each word.

| stripe | strong | strangers | street |

1.

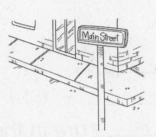

_____

- - - - - - - - - - - -

_____

2.

_____

- - - - - - - - - - - -

_____

3.

_____

- - - - - - - - - - - -

_____

4.

_____

- - - - - - - - - - - -

_____

Think about the story <u>When You Were Little</u>. Write a word from the box to complete each sentence.

> bedroom   boy   talking   mother

1. Who is in the story?

_____   _____

A _____ and his _____ are in the story.

2. What are they doing?

They are _____.

3. Where are they?

They are in the _____.

Name _____

Circle the contraction in each sentence.
Underline the words that make the contraction.

1. It isn't sunny outside.

is not   are not

2. The mice aren't big.

is not   are not

3. The rabbit isn't sleeping.

is not   are not

4. The horse isn't running.

is not   are not

5. The shoes aren't dirty.

is not   are not

Name _____

Read each sentence. Find the meaning of the boldfaced word in the box. Write the number of the correct meaning on the line.

> **saw**   1. the past tense of <u>see</u>
> 2. a tool for cutting things

1. Dad cuts wood with a **saw**. _____

2. Ann **saw** many birds in the park. _____

> **bat**   1. a stick used to hit a ball
> 2. a flying animal that has wings

3. He uses the **bat** to play baseball. _____

4. The **bat** flies through the air. _____

© Macmillan/McGraw-Hill

Name _____

Circle the word that names the picture.

1. nose   nut

2. bus   bone

3. rose   red

Circle the word with the long o sound.

4. hose   help

5. green   globe

6. match   cone

7. home   key

8. zone   card

Look at the pictures. Circle the letter of the sentence that tells what will happen next.

1.

    a.   The bird will look for food.

    b.   The bird will build a nest.

2.

    a.   The bird will feed its babies.

    b.   The bird will build a nest.

Name _____

Circle the word that completes each sentence. Write the word on the line.

_____
- - - - - - - - - -
1. The bird _____ in the nest.

   was   were

_____
- - - - - - - - - -
2. The nest _____ in the tree.

   was   were

_____
- - - - - - - - - -
3. There _____ many birds in the city.

   was   were

_____
- - - - - - - - - -
4. There _____ two eggs in the nest.

   was   were

Name _____

Circle the sentence that matches each picture.

1. Sara puts a bottle into a bin.

   Sara plays with toys.

2. I throw the ball.

   I give away old toys.

3. I draw Earth.

   I read books in the library.

4. I use old jugs to make flowerpots.

   She plants a tree.

Name _____

Circle the word that names the picture.

1. hug   huge

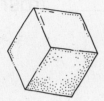

2. cube   cub

Circle the word that completes each sentence. Write the word on the line.

_____
_ _ _ _ _ _ _ _ _ _

3. I _____ a pencil to write.

   use   us

_____
_ _ _ _ _ _ _ _ _ _

4. My dog is _____.

   cut   cute

Name _____

Think about the story <u>Use It Again!</u> Write the word that completes each sentence on the line.

I. You can use paper again.

You can use old things to make new things.

_____

Using things again makes _____ trash.

more   less

2. You can take care of your things.

You can fix things that do not work.

_____

Taking care of your things _____ Earth.

helps   hurts

Name _____

Write a word from the box to complete each sentence.

> has   have

_____
- - - - - - - - - -

1. The boys _____ books.

_____
- - - - - - - - - -

2. Our class _____ bins.

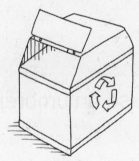

_____
- - - - - - - - - -

3. The bins _____ cans in them.

_____
- - - - - - - - - -

4. Mom _____ a paper bag.

Name _____

Read the definitions in the box. Write a word from the box to complete each sentence.

> **rain:** water that falls from clouds
> **snow:** frozen water that falls to the ground
> **wind:** air that moves
> **warm:** a little hot

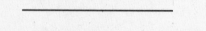

1. It is _____ outside.

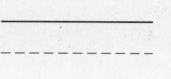

2. I use an umbrella in the _____.

3. I like to sled in the _____.

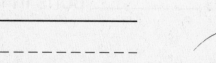

4. The _____ blows the trees.

© Macmillan/McGraw-Hill

Name _____

Circle the word with the long <u>a</u> sound.

1. say   set

2. ran   rain

3. pain   pen

4. play   pan

5. clap   clay

Circle the words that tell how the weather is the same.

Monday: warm and cloudy

Tuesday: cloudy and rainy

Circle the words that tell how the weather is different.

Thursday: windy and cold

Friday: snowy and windy

Name _____

Write a word from the box to complete each sentence.

go	do	does	goes

_____

1. What do you _____ on sunny days?

_____

2. I _____ to the beach.

_____

3. He _____ outside.

_____

4. _____ he need an umbrella?

_____

5. No, he _____ not need an umbrella.

Name _____

Circle the word that completes each sentence.

1. When Mae Jemison was a girl, she
_____ to look at the stars.

likes   liked

2. Now Mae Jemison _____ to teach.

likes   liked

Write the verb with the ending.

3. float + s =

_____

- - - - - - - - - -

_____

4. work + ed =

_____

- - - - - - - - - -

_____

5. fill + ed =

_____

- - - - - - - - - -

_____

Name _____

Circle the word that matches each picture.

1. me   my

2. bee   bell

3. tip   tea

4. shell   sheep

5. peach   pear

Name _____

Think about the story <u>Meet Mae Jemison</u>. Circle the word that completes each sentence.

1. **What I Read:**
   Mae Jemison went to space.

   What I Know:
   Stars are in space.

   Inference:
   Mae Jemison saw _____ in space.

   cars   stars

2. **What I Read:**
   Astronauts wear space suits.

   What I Know:
   Space suits have helmets.

   Inference:
   Mae Jemison wore a _____ in space.

   helmet   shuttle

Circle the word that completes each sentence. Write the word on the line.

1. What do you _____ ?

   see   saw

2. I can _____ the plane.

   see   saw

3. He _____ it last night.

   saw   see

4. Ken _____ it, too.

   see   saw

Name _____

Circle the letter of the sentence that matches each picture.

1.

    a. Grasshopper sings.

    b. Grasshopper saves food.

2.

    a. Ant eats food.

    b. Ant saves food for the winter.

3.

    a. Ant shares his food.

    b. Ant watches Grasshopper sing.

Name _____

Circle the word that completes each sentence. Write the word on the line.

_____
- - - - - - - - - -

1. It is a ——————— day.

sunny   easy

_____
- - - - - - - - - -

2. The ——————— jumps.

bun   bunny

_____
- - - - - - - - - -

3. The girl is ———————.

happy   help

_____
- - - - - - - - - -

4. He is ———————.

have   hungry

Name _____

**Think about The Ant and the Grasshopper.
Circle the word that completes each sentence.**

1. **Beginning:**
   Grasshopper sings. Ant saves _____.
   corn   snow

2. **Middle:**
   _____ does not want to save food.
   Ant   Grasshopper

3. **End:**
   Ant gives _____ to Grasshopper.
   food   snow

**Read each sentence. Circle when
each event happened.**

4. Ant collects corn.   summer   winter

5. Ant gives food to Grasshopper.   summer   winter

Write the contraction for the boldfaced words on the line.

don't	doesn't	hasn't	haven't

1. Grasshopper **does not** save food. _____

2. Grasshopper **has not** worked at all. _____

3. Ant and Grasshopper **do not** work together. _____

4. They **have not** eaten the food. _____

© Macmillan/McGraw-Hill

Name _____

Draw a line to match the picture to the sentence.

1.

2.

3.

a. Kim shuts the car door.

b. Jay shuts his eyes.

c. Jon shuts off the water.

Write a word from the box to complete each sentence.

> **supposed:** <u>verb</u> thought, believed
> **smiled:** <u>verb</u> made a happy face

_____
- - - - - - - - - -

4. Angie _____ that Kate
was going to be late.

5. Angie was happy to see Kate.

_____
- - - - - - - - - -

She _____ at her friend.

Circle the word that names each picture.

1.

   Joan   jar

2.

   row   rake

3.

   ship   story

Draw a line under the letters that make the long o sound.

4. tow

5. boat

6. open

7. goat

**Think about the story Hopscotch Daydream.
Circle fantasy or reality for each sentence.**

1. Joan plays hopscotch with Liz and Maria.
   fantasy   reality

2. Joan saw people with funny outfits. Joan had a funny
   outfit too.
   fantasy   reality

3. Joan said, "I love hopscotch." Liz said, "I love it too."
   fantasy   reality

4. The people in the painting were moving and playing.
   fantasy   reality

**Write fantasy if the sentence is something that could
not happen. Write reality if the sentence is something
that could happen.**

5. We rode our bicycles on the

   _____
   - - - - - - - - - -
   clouds. _____
           _____
           - - - - - - - - - - -

6. Joan is a fast runner. _____
                          _____
                          - - - - - - - - - -

7. Marcia likes to fly to school. _____

Name _____

Write an adjective from the box to tell about each picture.

sleepy	new	big
small	fun	

Example:

ride _____

fun
_____

1.

ball _____

_____

2.

bike _____

_____

3.

square _____

_____

4.

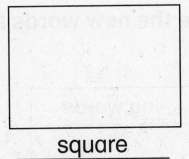

puppy _____

_____

Add -ed or -ing to each word in ( ). Write the new word on the line.

1. Nicky _____ the book.
   _ _ _ _ _ _ _ _ _ _
   (push)

2. Mike is _____ the wagon.
   _ _ _ _ _ _ _ _ _ _
   (pull)

3. The baby _____ out loud.
   _ _ _ _ _ _ _ _ _ _
   (shout)

Add -ed and -ing to each verb. Write the new words in the chart.

Verb	-ed words	-ing words
head		
float		

Name _____

Circle the word that names each picture.

1.

felt   fly

2.

child   hello

3.

high   help

Write the word with the long i sound on the line.

4.   dry   drip   _____

5.   mint   mind   _____

6.   right   read   _____

Think about the story Teddy Helps. Circle the letter that tells how Teddy helped.

1. **Problem:** The door shut on Rabbit.

   Solution:
   a. Teddy pulled the door open.
   b. Teddy asked Rabbit for help.

2. **Problem:** Matt shouted, "Mouse will go in the glue."

   Solution:
   a. Teddy put glue on Mouse.
   b. Teddy pushed Mouse away.

3. **Problem:** Pam shouted, "My doll fell into the water."

   Solution:
   a. Teddy looked at the doll.
   b. Teddy pulled the doll out.

© Macmillan/McGraw-Hill

Name _____

Circle the adjective that completes each sentence.

1. Sara is (taller, tallest) than Ed.

2. This doll is (smaller, smallest) than that doll.

3. My friend is (shorter, shortest) than me.

4. My cat is the (smarter, smartest) cat of all.

Draw a big box in the first square. Draw a bigger box in the second square. Draw the biggest box in the third square.

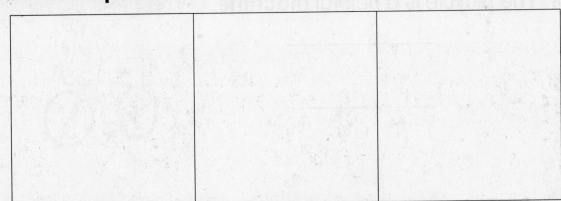

big box   bigger box   biggest box

**Write a synonym from the box for each
word in dark print.**

> **tool:** *noun* something that makes a job easier
> **creation:** *noun* something you make or invent
> **kids:** *noun* young people; not grown-ups

1. Many **children** like to ride bicycles.

_____

- - - - - - - - - - -

_____

2. The bicycle was an **invention** from long ago.

_____

_____

3. The bicycle is a helpful **machine**.

_____

- - - - - - - - - - -

_____

© Macmillan/McGraw-Hill

Name _____

Circle the word with the <u>ar</u> sound.

1. far   fair

2. hair   hard

3. pail   park

Write a letter or letters from the box to complete the words. You can use each letter more than once.

A   R   C

4. ____ ar

5. f ____ m

6. sh ____ k

Name _____

Circle the letter of the effect for each cause.

1. **Cause:** The first bicycle had
   no pedals.

   Effect: a. Someone added
   pedals to the bicycle.

   b. Bicycles did not
   need pedals.

2. **Cause:** Long ago bicycles had one
   big wheel and one small wheel.

   Effect: a. The bicycle was
   hard to ride.

   b. The bicycle was very
   fast.

3. **Cause:** There are signs on the
   street to keep riders safe.

   Effect: a. Bikers should read the
   signs carefully.

   b. The signs are
   pretty.

© Macmillan/McGraw-Hill

**Circle the color word in each sentence.
Then color the pictures.**

1. I pull the red wagon.

2. The grass in our yard is green.

3. My dad has a blue car.

4. She gives her mother purple flowers.

**Color the bicycle. Write the
name of the color to complete
the sentence.**

The bike is _____

Name _____

Circle the word that completes each sentence.

1. Sara is _____ in her pool.

   swims   swimming

2. I _____ this morning.

   yawns   yawned

3. Molly _____ me with a present.

   surprising   surprised

4. Rose _____ some flowers for her mom.

   picked   picking

Write now if the action is happening now.
Write past if the action happened in the past.

5. is sleeping _____

6. climbed _____

7. is calling _____

8. mowed _____

Name _____

Draw a line to match the word to the picture.

1.   corn

2.   horse

3.   storm

Circle each word with the <u>or</u> sound.

4.   flake   fort

5.   make   more

6.   cord   cake

7.   door   lake

8.   snake   chore

Name _____

Circle the sentence that tells about the picture.

1. Jimmy is a good swimmer.

Jimmy doesn't like the water.

2. Ms. Castro is Jimmy's swimming teacher

Ms. Castro is Jimmy's reading teacher.

3. Angela needs to go to school.

Angela's father needs to go to school.

Name _____

Draw a line to match the words with the pictures.

1. four shells

2. two dolphins

3. six bubbles

4. one girl

5. three dogs

Name _____

Circle the words that tell about the word in dark print.

1. The **tiny** seed was hard to see.

2. Beavers, squirrels, and other **animals** live in the forest.

3. We like to **pick** apples from trees in the spring.

4. The basket was **crowded** with too many fruits.

Use one of the words in dark print to name the pictures below.

5.

_____

- - - - - - - - - - - - - - -

_____

6.

_____

- - - - - - - - - - - - - - -

_____

© Macmillan/McGraw-Hill

Name _____

Circle the word with the <u>ur</u> sound.

1. hill   hurt

2. dirt   dog

3. power   poor

Write a word from the box to complete each sentence.

turkey	flower	shirt

4. He puts on a clean _____.

5. She smells the _____.

6. The _____ is running.

Write the words from the box that tell about apples. Then write the words that tell about apple trees.

have flowers	people eat them
are tall	are round

Apples:

1. _____

2. _____

Apple Trees:

3. _____

4. _____

Think about the story, How Do Apples Grow? What colors can apples be? Color the pictures below.

Circle the synonym of each word.

Word	Synonym	
1. big	large	medium
2. small	glad	tiny
3. cold	chilly	red

Circle the antonym of each word.

Word	Antonym	
4. big	tall	tiny
5. small	big	pretty
6. cold	hot	mad

Name _____

Read the definitions below. Circle the word that belongs to each definition. Write it on the line.

1. Definition:
a small animal with six legs

bug   dog

_____

- - - - - - - - - -

_____

2. Definition:
a flying bug that makes honey

bee   bear

_____

- - - - - - - - - -

_____

3. Definition:
a place where bees live

hive   home

_____

- - - - - - - - - -

_____

4. Definition:
a tall plant that has branches

dirt   tree

_____

- - - - - - - - - -

_____

Name _____

Draw a line to match the word with the picture.

1. cow

2. mouse

3. clown

4. mouth

Circle the word with the <u>ow</u> sound.

5.   crown   moose

6.   soup   house

Name _____

Read about the picture.
Write a word to complete each sentence.

Bees live in a hive. Bees build their hives high off the ground. The hive must face the sun. The sun keeps the bees warm.

sun	hive	bee	tree

_____

1. Bees live in a _____.

_____

2. This hive is in a _____.

_____

3. The _____ shines on the bees.

_____

4. A _____ is in the hive.

© Macmillan/McGraw-Hill

Name _____

Circle the subject in each sentence.

1. Bee flew out of her hive.   **2.** The hive is in a tree.

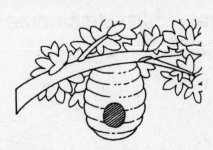

3. The tree is tall.   **4.** A bug was on a flower.

5. The flower is pretty.   **6.** The bees flew back to their hive.

Name _____

Circle the correct meaning for each word in dark print. Use clues from the picture and the sentences.

1. The **helmet** will keep his head safe if he falls.

hard hat   soft hat

2. He studies **space**.

a place where   a store
there are stars

3. The spaceship **lands** on Earth.

comes up   comes down

4. The space people **visit** the Bear family.

live with   stay a short
time

Name _____

Circle the word that names the picture.
Write the word on the line.

1.

book   boat

_____

- - - - - - - - - - -

_____

2.

coat   cook

_____

- - - - - - - - - - -

3.

wind   wood

_____

- - - - - - - - - - -

_____

4.

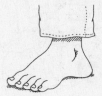

foot   food

_____

- - - - - - - - - - -

_____

Name _____

Read each sentence. Circle <u>yes</u> or <u>no</u> to tell what could happen next.

1. Tina will find her pencil.   yes   no

2. Mike will read a book.   yes   no

Think about the story <u>A Good Little Visit</u>. Circle <u>yes</u> or <u>no</u> to tell what happens.

3. The space people stay with the
   Bear family.   yes   no

4. Little Bear has a good visit with
   the space people.   yes   no

What words tell what Bear did? Circle the predicate in each sentence.

1. Bear looks at the sky.

2. Bear tells his mother about the space people.

3. Bear eats with the space people.

4. Bear rides in a spaceship.

Name _____

Circle the antonym for the word in dark print.

1. **go**   stay   try

2. **sick**   sneeze   well

3. **laugh** smile   cry

4. **better** sad   worse

Circle the word with the <u>oo</u> sound that completes each sentence. Write the word on the line.

_____

- - - - - - - -

1. I like to go to the _____.

      zoo   work

_____

- - - - - - - - -

2. The horse eats _____.

      food   fat

_____

- - - - - - - - -

3. I put the _____ on my feet.

      boots   balls

_____

- - - - - - - - -

4. My _____ hurts!

      mouth   tooth

_____

- - - - - - - - -

5. I clean the floor with a _____.

      broom   brown

Name _____

Complete the chart. Write the names of the animals that belong in the same group.

hen

horse

dog

duck

cat

penguin

Animals With Two Legs	Animals With Four Legs
1. _____	4. _____
2. _____	5. _____
3. _____	6. _____

Name _____

Circle the pronoun that takes the place of the word in dark print. Write it on the line.

1. A **dog** has four legs.   It   We

   _____

   - - - - - - - - - - -

   _____ has four legs.

2. **The vet** takes care of animals.   She   We

   _____

   - - - - - - - - - -

   _____ takes care of animals.

3. **My brother** likes animals.   He   They

   _____

   - - - - - - - - - -

   _____ likes animals.

4. Sometimes **animals** get sick.   they   she

   _____

   - - - - - - - - -

   Sometimes _____ get sick.

5. **My brother and I** have a pet cat.   We   They

   _____

   - - - - - - - - - -

   _____ have a pet cat.

Cross out the -ed or -ing ending. Then write the root word.

1. called

    _____   _____

2. jumping

    _____   _____

3. learning

    _____   _____

4. crawled

    _____   _____

Circle the verb in each sentence. Write the root word on the line.

5. The fawn is looking at me.

    _____

6. We are watching a show.

    _____

Circle the word with the <u>aw</u> sound that names the picture.

1.

pot   paw

2.

fun   fawn

Circle the word with the <u>aw</u> sound.

3.   draw   dress   dream

4.   faucet   face   fin

5.   soap   saucer   sock

How are a buck and a fawn alike? How are they different? Write a word from the box to complete each sentence.

spots   antlers   animals   fur

_____

1. **Different:** A fawn has _____ on its fur.

_____

2. **Different:** A buck has _____ on its head.

_____

3. **Same:** Both have _____ on their bodies.

_____

4. **Same:** Both are _____.

Name _____

Circle the word that completes each sentence.
Write the word on the line.

_____

1. _____ read a book about deer.

      I   me

_____

2. _____ like forest animals.

      I   me

_____

3. Mother takes _____ to the zoo.

      I   me

_____

4. _____ see a deer at the zoo.

      I   me

_____

5. The buck looks at _____ .

      I   me

Circle the correct meaning for each word in dark print. Use clues from the picture and the sentence.

1. Carlos rides home on his **new** bike.

just bought   old

2. Carlos makes a **circle** with the blocks.

round shape   square shape

3. They want to play **outside**.

inside a building   not inside a building

4. Carlos and Andy play **together**.

alone   with each other

Name _____

Draw a line to match the word to the picture.

1. toys

2. coin

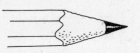

3. point

Circle the word that completes each sentence.
Write the word on the line.

_____

4. I want to _____ the soccer team.

    join   June

_____

5. She has a loud _____.

    boot   voice

Name _____

Think about the story <u>The Playhouse</u>. Circle the word that completes each sentence.

I. Miss Kent helps Carlos because he is _____.

       new   happy

2. It is raining so the class can not _____.

      go outside   read books

3. Miss Kent gives Carlos blocks so he builds a _____.

      garden   house

4. Carlos is happy because he _____.

      made friends   fell down

Use the word *and* to put the sentences together.
Write the new sentence on the line.

1. He plays with his dog. He plays with his cat.

_____

- -

_____

2. The girls want to play outside. The boys want to play
outside.

_____

- -

_____

3. The girl sits in the classroom. The girl reads.

_____

- -

_____

4. Carlos makes a playhouse. Andy makes a playhouse.

_____

- -

_____